2023 LOW BUYERS GUIDE

2023
LOW-CARB
BUYERS GUIDE

Discover the ultimate list of community-voted top products that will make your mouth water

JOSH SCHIEFFER

Table of Contents

How To Read:

Example - Chips

2023 Annual Low-Carb Awards

1st Place Winner: Whisps Parmesan All Natural Cheese Crisps

2nd Place Winner: BeyondChipz Keto Tortilla Chips Salty Good

3rd Place Winner: Unsupervised Nacho Cheese Keto Chips

Runner Up:

Genius Gourmet Chili Lime Chips

Other Great Products:

Quest Protein Chips – Ranch

Introduction by Josh Schieffer

This happens to be our 14th year producing consumer-based award programs and we are excited to connect you to the results. If you are not familiar with the guide, I thought it would be best to explain what it is and more importantly what it is not.

Each year, brands and respected low-carb personalities register products into our consumer voting ballot. For a month, we push that ballot to the low-carb community allowing them to vote for their favorite products on the ballot. We publish the buyers guide with the award results organized by category. Nothing fancy, just consumers helping consumers, the way it should be.

This book is much more than a list of great low-carb products to buy, we also list some of the best low-carb personalities. Being on a low-carb diet can be isolating in so many ways and difficult at first.

This book does not contain every single low-carb product available in every market. The food industry has changed dramatically since we started in 2008. Virtually no regional grocery chains had private label low-carb products and now it is the norm with west coast chains like Safeway and east coast chains like Publix. We tend to focus on brands with national distribution and national grocery chains. We do this so you have access to these products regardless of where you live. Oftentimes ordering online can save you money, time and widen your options dramatically.

You will not find every brand or product listed in this book on your local grocery shelves. It's a strange fact to some but often brands must pay to sit on the shelves of most grocery stores. This is especially true for products that don't get purchased as often, like low-carb products. If you have a favorite product that your store doesn't carry, you can request that they stock it for a trial period. If it sells, more than likely they will keep it without the brand paying for the space. However, if a competing brand buys out the shelf space your product will more than likely disappear. This is the cold hard truth about the industry. Those who eat low-carb food to maintain a healthy lifestyle ultimately pay the price. Oftentimes low-carb food is medicine for a diagnosis or health situation we didn't want or ask for. Please use this guide to help make your low-carb lifestyle the best it can be.

Why do I tell you all of this? Those of us with restricted diets have limited options especially in rural parts of the country. I do not want your diet and the products you eat being dictated by what brands pay to sit on your local shelves. The product placement in your local store is not based on how great the product is and how well it tastes. If you want to have the best low-carb products in your pantry, more than likely you will need to travel to multiple stores and order online.

At the end of the day, I want you to know that there are great low-carb products for you. If you are new to the low-carb diet or just struggling to maintain the diet because of product availability or poor product quality, we published this book for you. Please read "Our Story" so you have a better understanding of why we have hundreds of product pictures and not just a list of a million random low-carb products.

Our Story

The story behind The Guided Buyer that very few people know

I remember it like it was yesterday when my four-year-old son Jacob, now eighteen, was playing in the kiddie pool with other kids that I assumed were his age based on their height. After asking all the surrounding kids what ages they were, I realized Jacob was significantly smaller than kids his own age. This prompted my wife and I to seek a professional opinion. After consulting with our family physician, she confirmed that Jacob had essentially stopped growing for an entire year without us realizing it. He was referred to Jeff Gordon's Children's Hospital in Charlotte North Carolina to discuss possible growth hormone therapy. The doctors there reviewed Jacob's case and requested a few blood tests based on some suspicions they had.

Our cell phone service at our house was terrible so when the doctor finally called with the blood results, my wife and I ran to the front of the driveway to hear the doctor clearly. With a sporadic signal, we heard "Jacob has celiac disease." We looked at each other as tears ran down my wife's face. We huddled closer to the phone and asked, "what is celiac disease?". After getting a brief description mixed with crappy cell service and happy neighbors waving as they drove by, my wife and I embraced and wept. We were told to maintain his normal diet until we could have an endoscopy and biopsy for further confirmation. Once confirmed our next visit was to a registered dietitian for guidance.

Jayme, my wife, made the appointment and called me with a weird request. "Will you meet me at the dietitian's house for a consultation?". I was confused when she said to go to her house. Jayme then explained that the dietician's daughter had celiac disease too and the best way to show the new lifestyle to patients would be to dive right in. I'll admit, it was a bit uncomfortable at first to be in a strangers' house looking at their personal items but looking back now, I wouldn't change it for the world. That encounter is ultimately the motivation behind the consumer awards and the associated buyers guides. We left her house with complete understanding of best practices and what products they personally liked and disliked. That visit was life changing and left us feeling confident as we made our way to the local health food store.

That first trip shopping took forever. Each label was read, and cross checked with our list of known gluten containing suspects. It was also shocking to see the bill when it was time to pay. We had replaced our entire pantry and fridge with all products that had the "gluten-free" label. We both worked full-time and had decent paying jobs and it still set us back financially.

We looked for support groups locally and came across a "100% Gluten-Free Picnic" in Raleigh, which was two hours away from where we lived. This was our first time meeting other people with celiac disease and we were fortunate to have met some informative people that were willing to help with the hundreds of questions we had. We were introduced to a family whose son had been recently diagnosed with celiac disease as well. His condition was much worse than Jacobs and he was almost hospitalized before finally being diagnosed. They confided in us as we shared similar stories. There were two key differences that would light a motivational fire I could not extinguish. The first was the fact that they didn't have the same experience with a registered dietitian. Instead, they were handed a two-page Xerox copy of "safe foods". Second, they didn't have the financial security to experiment with gluten-free counterparts. Their first two months exposed to the gluten free lifestyle left them extremely depressed and financially broke.

On our way home from that picnic, Jayme and I felt compelled to help make a difference in some way. We were determined to help that family and others being diagnosed with this disease. Up until that day, we hadn't found a resource that gave unbiased opinions on gluten free products and services. Fast forward a few years and I too was diagnosed with celiac disease. That year, The Gluten-Free Awards were born.

Originally our vision was to create a one-page website with a handful of categories organized by peoples' favorites. Each year we grew; more products, more categories, and eventually a buyers guide by request. For years we had been asked to produce similar programs and buyer guides for other diets. In 2020 we expanded yet again with adding three new diets to our consumer awards programs. We now host:

The Gluten Free Awards & Buyers Guide

The Low-Carb Awards & Buyers Guide

The Plant Based Awards & Buyers Guide

The Dairy Free Awards & Buyers Guide

We want to thank those special people and organizations that brought us to where we are today:

Pat Fogarty MS, RD, LDN for allowing us to enter your home.

Jeff Gordon's Children's Hospital

Raleigh Celiac Support Groups

Dean Meisel, MD, FAAP for the excellent medical care he provides for our family.

I hope you have learned something new from the story behind The Guided Buyer. Today, Jacob and I continue to live a healthy lifestyle.

Bread & Bakery

Bagels

2023 Annual Low-Carb Awards

1st Place Winner: Unbun Bagels Everything

2nd Place Winner: Everything Bagel from Pagels

3rd Place Winner: ThinSlim Foods Love-the-Taste Bagels Everything Inside

Runner Up:

Carbonaut Plain Bagels

Other Great Products:

ALDI-exclusive L'oven Fresh Keto Friendly Bagels

Bread

2023 Annual Low-Carb Awards

1st Place Winner: ALDI-exclusive L'oven Fresh Keto Friendly Buns

2nd Place Winner: Kiss My Keto Bread — Cinnamon Raisin

3rd Place Winner: Carbonaut White Bread

Runner Up:

Sola Sweet and Buttery Bread

Other Great Products:

Carbonaut Seeded Bread

Breadcrumbs

2023 Annual Low-Carb Awards

1st Place Winner: Kiss My Keto Bread Crumbs Everything Seasoned

2nd Place Winner: Yez! Foods Artisan Keto Bread Crumbs

3rd Place Winner: Kiss My Keto Bread Crumbs Classic

Runner Up:

Pork King Good Pork Rind Breadcrumbs

Other Great Products:

Appel Foods Nut Crumbs Original

Buns

2023 Annual Low-Carb Awards

1st Place Winner: Smart Baking Company Smartbuns

2nd Place Winner: Sola Low Carb & Keto Friendly Golden Wheat Hamburger Buns

3rd Place Winner: ThinSlim Foods Low Carb Hamburger Buns

Runner Up:

Unbun

Other Great Buns:

Carbonaut Buns

Cookies

2023 Annual Low-Carb Awards

1st Place Winner: Quest Nutrition Chocolate Chip Protein Cookies

2nd Place Winner: Highkey Mini Chocolate Chip Cookies

3rd Place Winner: Fat Snax Chocolate Chip Keto Cookies

Runner Up:

Nunbelievable Low Carb Pecan Sandy Cookies

Other Great Products:

Perfect Keto Cookies Chocolate Chip

Pizza Crust

2023 Annual Low-Carb Awards

1st Place Winner: Banza Plain Chickpea Pizza Crust

2nd Place Winner: Cappello's, Naked Pizza Crust

3rd Place Winner: Uncrust by Unbun

Runner Up:

BFree Stone Baked Pizza Crust

Other Great Products:

Trader Joe's Cauliflower Crust

Rolls

2023 Annual Low-Carb Awards

1st Place Winner: Ener-G Gluten Free Keto Rolls

2nd Place Winner: ThinSlim Foods Rustic Tuscan Olive and Garlic Rolls

3rd Place Winner: Keto Factory Cinnamon Rolls Mix

Tortilla

2023 Annual Low-Carb Awards

1st Place Winner: Mission Carb Balance Flour Tortilla

2nd Place Winner: 365 by Whole Foods Market Almond Flour Tortillas

3rd Place Winner: untortillas by unbun

Runner Up:

Mr. Tortilla 1 Net Carb Tortillas

Other Great Products:

A La Madre Low Carb Corn Tortillas

Wrap

2023 Annual Low-Carb Awards

1st Place Winner: BFree Foods High Protein Carb Friendly

2nd Place Winner: Wrap Wonder Wraps - Original

3rd Place Winner: Julian Bakery Keto Thin Wraps

Runner Up:

Flatout Protein Up

Other Great Products:

Mr. Tortilla Low Carb Tortillas

Breakfast

Breakfast On-The-Go

2023 Annual Low-Carb Awards

1st Place Winner: Jimmy Dean Simple Scrambles Bacon

2nd Place Winner:

Legendary Foods Tasty Pastry Toaster Pastries

3rd Place Winner: Pirq Caramel Coffee Protein Shake

Runner Up:

The Elite Donut – Chocolate

Other Great Products:

HighKey Banana Bread Soft Baked Breakfast Biscuit

Cold Cereals

2023 Annual Low-Carb Awards

1st Place Winner: Three Wishes Honey Breakfast Cereal

2nd Place Winner: Magic Spoon Fruity Cereal

3rd Place Winner: Kay's Naturals Honey Almond Protein Cereal

Runner Up:

Magic Spoon Maple Waffle

Other Great Products:

Snack House Chocolate Puffs

Donuts

2023 Annual Low-Carb Awards

1st Place Winner: Elite Sweets The Elite Donut Cinnamon Sugar

2nd Place Winner: WOW! Cake Batter Protein Donut

3rd Place Winner: Elite Sweets The Elite Donut Chocolate

Runner Up:

Maui Keto Treats Chocolate Cream Sweet Cake Donut Keto Baking Mix

Other Great Products:

WOW! Chocolate Protein Donut

Frozen Pancake & Waffle Brands

2023 Annual Low-Carb Awards

1st Place Winner: Kashi GO Frozen Wild Blueberry Protein Waffles

2nd Place Winner: Birch Benders Gluten Free Keto Frozen Waffles Chocolate Chip

3rd Place Winner: Birch Benders Gluten Free Keto Frozen Waffles

Runner Up:

Birch Benders Paleo Toaster Waffles

Other Great Products:

Kashi GO Frozen Cinnamon Brown Sugar Protein Waffles

Pancake and Waffle Mixes

2023 Annual Low-Carb Awards

1st Place Winner: Birch Benders Paleo Pancake & Waffle Mix

2nd Place Winner: King Arthur Carb-Conscious Keto Pancake Mix

3rd Place Winner: Keto and Co. Low Carb Pancake & Waffle Mix

Runner Up:

Good Dee's Pancakes Plus

Other Great Products:

Lakanto Pancake and Baking Mix

Yogurt

2023 Annual Low-Carb Awards

1st Place Winner: Two Good Low-fat Lower Sugar Strawberry Greek Yogurt

2nd Place Winner: Kite Hill Vanilla Greek Style Almond Milk Yogurt

3rd Place Winner: :ratio KETO Friendly Dairy Snack - Strawberry

Runner Up:

Chobani Zero Sugar Vanilla

Other Great Products:

Two Good Low-fat Lower Sugar Lemon Greek Yogurt

Cookies, Snacks & Candy

Candy

2023 Annual Low-Carb Awards

1st Place Winner: ChocZero 70% Dark Chocolate

2nd Place Winner: SlimFast Keto Fat Bomb Peanut Butter Cups

3rd Place Winner: Tom & Jenny's Classic Sugar Free Soft Caramels

Runner Up:

Smart Sweets Sourmelon Bites

Other Great Products:

Lily's Chocolate Bar 40% with Caramel and Sea Salt

Chips

2023 Annual Low-Carb Awards

1st Place Winner: Whisps Parmesan All Natural Cheese Crisps

2nd Place Winner: Genius Gourmet Chili Lime Chips

3rd Place Winner: BeyondChipz Keto Tortilla Chips Salty Good

Runner Up:

Unsupervised Nacho Cheese Keto Chips

Other Great Products:

Quest Protein Chips – Ranch

Crackers

2023 Annual Low-Carb Awards

1st Place Winner: Julian Bakery Paleo Thin Salt & Pepper Crackers

2nd Place Winner: Fat Snax Almond Flour Crackers

3rd Place Winner: HighKey Cheddar Cheese Crackers

Runner Up:

Keto Naturals Sea Salt Crackers

Other Great Products:

Innofoods Keto Crackers

Granola

2023 Annual Low-Carb Awards

1st Place Winner: Purely Elizabeth Vanilla Almond Butter Keto Granola Clusters

2nd Place Winner: simplyFUEL Keto Nut Granola

3rd Place Winner: Bakery On Main Low Sugar Granola

Runner Up:

NuTrail™ Keto Vanilla Strawberry Nut Granola

Other Great Products:

TGB Keto Candied Pecans with Cinnamon Nut Granola

Sola Maple Pecan Chocolate

Jerky

2023 Annual Low-Carb Awards

1st Place Winner: Jack Link's Zero Sugar Beef Jerky Original Flavor

2nd Place Winner: Old Wisconsin Turkey Sausage Snack Sticks

3rd Place Winner: CHOMPS Grass Fed Original Beef Jerky Meat Snack Sticks

Runner Up:

Baja Crackin' Pepper Beef Jerky

Other Great Products:

paleovalley Grass Fed Beef Sticks

Munchies

2023 Annual Low-Carb Awards

1st Place Winner: Blue Diamond Almonds Oven Roasted Dark Chocolate Almonds

2nd Place Winner: ChocZero's Dark Chocolate Almonds with Sea Salt Keto Bark

3rd Place Winner: Quest Nutrition Loaded Taco Tortilla Style Protein Chips

Runner Up:

Catalina Crunch Chocolate Vanilla Keto Cookies

Other Great Products:

Eat Different -   Right Out Of The Jar, Edible Cookie Dough

innofoods Keto Clusters

Pretzels

2023 Annual Low-Carb Awards

1st Place Winner: Quinn Original Paleo Friendly Pretzel Chip

2nd Place Winner: Kay's Naturals Protein Pretzel Sticks Jalapeno Honey Mustard

3rd Place Winner: WonderSlim High Protein Pretzel Snacks

Runner Up:

Catalina Crunch Creamy Ranch Crunch Mix

Other Great Products:

Kays Protein Pretzel Sticks Cinnamon Toast

Snack Bars

2023 Annual Low-Carb Awards

1st Place Winner: Quest Nutrition Cookies & Cream Protein Bar

2nd Place Winner: Munk Pack Coconut Cocoa Chip Keto Granola Bar

3rd Place Winner: Just The Cheese – Grilled Cheese Snack Bar

Runner Up:

CanDo Keto Krisp Almond Butter

Other Great Products:

GOOD TO GO Blueberry Cashew Snack Bar

Desserts

Ice Cream Brands

2023 Annual Low-Carb Awards

1st Place Winner: Rebel

2nd Place Winner: Enlightened

3rd Place Winner: Halo Top

Runner Up:

Arctic Zero

Other Great Products:

Breyers Carb Smart

Ice Cream Cones

2023 Annual Low-Carb Awards

1st Place Winner: Enlightened Sugar-Free Cones

Pie Crust

2023 Annual Low-Carb Awards

1st Place Winner: Fifty50 Foods Sugar Free Ready to Eat Graham Cracker Pie Crust

2nd Place Winner: Kbosh Keto Crusts

3rd Place Winner: Sooo Ketolicious Premium Keto Pie Crust

Runner Up:

Diamond Pecan Pie Crust

Ready Made Desserts

2023 Annual Low-Carb Awards

1st Place Winner: Quest Nutrition Fudgey Brownie Candy Bites

2nd Place Winner: Atkins Endulge Treat Strawberry Cheesecake Dessert Bar

3rd Place Winner: Rebel Coffee Chip Ice Cream

Runner Up:

Rebel Mint Chip

Other Great Products:

Sugar-Free Jell-O Chocolate Pudding Cups

Beverages

Beer

2023 Annual Low-Carb Awards

1ˢᵗ Place Winner: Dogfish Head Slightly Mighty IPA

2ⁿᵈ Place Winner: Corona Premier

3ʳᵈ Place Winner: Michelob Ultra

Runner Up:

Lagunitas DayTime IPA

Other Great Beers:

Omission Ultimate Light Golden Ale

Creamers

2023 Annual Low-Carb Awards

1st Place Winner: nutpods Zero-Sugar Caramel Coffee Creamer

2nd Place Winner: Califia Farms - Unsweetened Almond Milk Coffee Creamer with Coconut Cream

3rd Place Winner: Laird's Unsweetened Liquid Superfood Creamer

Runner Up:

Lucerne Sugar Free Hazelnut Creamer.

Other Great Creamers:

RAPID FIRE Ketogenic Creamer Original Flavor

Ready-to-Drink Beverages

2023 Annual Low-Carb Awards

1st Place Winner: Koia Keto Ready To Drink Cake Batter Plant Protein Keto Shake

2nd Place Winner: SlimFast Advanced Nutrition Strawberries & Cream Meal Replacement Protein Shake

3rd Place Winner: Premier Cookies & Cream Protein Shake

Runner Up: Genius Gourmet All Natural Ready to Drink
Keto Chocolate Shake

Other Great Creamers:

Atkins Milk Chocolate Delight

Quest Salted Caramel Shake

Dry Mixes

Bread Mixes

2023 Annual Low-Carb Awards

1st Place Winner: Good Dee's Low Carb Multi-Purpose Bread Mix

2nd Place Winner: Scotty's Everyday Zero Carb Keto Bread Mix

3rd Place Winner: Livlo Biscuit Keto Baking Mix

Runner Up:

Livlo Bread Loaf Keto Baking Mix

Other Great Products:

Lakanto Sugar free Pumpkin Spice Muffin and Bread Mix

Brownie Mixes

2023 Annual Low-Carb Awards

1st Place Winner: Miss Jones Baking Keto Brownie Mix

2nd Place Winner: Keto and Co Keto Fudge Brownie Mix

3rd Place Winner: HighKey Snacks Keto Brownie Baking Mix

Runner Up:

Livlo Keto Brownie Baking Mix

Other Great Products:

Pyure Organic Chocolate Fudge Brownie Mix

Cake Mixes

2023 Annual Low-Carb Awards

1st Place Winner: Duncan Hines Keto Friendly Classic Yellow Cake Mix

2nd Place Winner: Swerve Sweets Vanilla Cake Mix

3rd Place Winner: Good Dee's Low Carb Devil's Food Cake Baking Mix

Runner Up:

Keto Queen Kreations Low Carb Pound Cake

Other Great Products:

Fit Bake Yellow Cake Baking Mix

Cookie Mixes

2023 Annual Low-Carb Awards

1st Place Winner: Good Dee's Low Carb Chocolate Chip Cookie Mix

2nd Place Winner: Keto and Co Shortbread Keto Cookie Mix

3rd Place Winner: Lakanto Double Chocolate Cookie Mix

Runner Up:

Kalifornia Keto Chocolate Chip Cookie Mix

Other Great Products:

Swerve Sweets Chocolate Chip Cookie Mix

Cornbread Mixes

2023 Annual Low-Carb Awards

1st Place Winner: Miss Jones Baking Not Cornbread Keto Muffin Mix

2nd Place Winner: No Sugar Aloud Low Carb Corn Bread Mix

3rd Place Winner: Good Dee's Corn Bread Baking Mix

Runner Up:

Kodiak Cakes Cornbread Mix

Other Great Products:

Highkey Bread and Muffin Mix Cornbread

Flours

2023 Annual Low-Carb Awards

1st Place Winner: King Arthur Keto Wheat Flour Blend

2nd Place Winner: Blue Diamond Almond Flour

3rd Place Winner: Bob's Red Mill Paleo Baking Flour

Runner Up:

Lo! Foods Ultra Low Carb Flour

Other Great Products:

Otto's Naturals Cassava Flour

Anthony's Almond Flour

Muffin Mixes

2023 Annual Low-Carb Awards

1st Place Winner: Keto & Co. Low Carb Banana Caramel Muffin Mix

2nd Place Winner: Highkey Blueberry Muffin & Cupcake Baking Mix

3rd Place Winner: Diabetic Kitchen Cheesy Bread Muffin Mix

Runner Up:

FlapJacked Peanut Butter Mighty Muffin Cups

Other Great Products:

Lakanto Blueberry Muffin MIx

Frozen Foods

Frozen Food / Meals

2023 Annual Low-Carb Awards

1st Place Winner: Real Good Foods Sausage & Egg Breakfast Sandwich

2nd Place Winner: Primal Kitchen Chicken Pesto Bowl

3rd Place Winner: ALDI-exclusive Simply Nature Cherry Berry Keto Smoothies

Runner Up:

Red's Egg'Wich Turkey Sausage

Other Great Products:

ALDI-exclusive Simply Nature Pineapple Greens Keto Smoothies

Frozen Pizza

2023 Annual Low-Carb Awards

1st Place Winner: Cappello's Uncured Pepperoni Pizza

2nd Place Winner: Cali'flour Foods Pizza Uncured Chicken Pepperoni

3rd Place Winner: Quest Nutrition Uncured Pepperoni Frozen Thin Crust Pizza

Runner Up:

Atkins Stone Fired Pepperoni Pizza

Other Great Products:

Quest Loaded Pizza

Books

Books

2023 Annual Low-Carb Awards

1st Place Winner: End Your Carb Confusion: A Simple Guide to Customize Your Carb Intake for Optimal Health by Dr. Eric Westman (Author), Amy Berger MS CNS (Author)

2nd Place Winner: Carnivore Code: Unlocking the Secrets to Optimal Health by Returning to Our Ancestral Diet by Paul Saladino

3rd Place Winner: Low-Carb Dieting For Dummies by Katherine B. Chauncey

Runner Up: The Complete Ketogenic Diet for Beginners: Your Essential Guide to Living the Keto Lifestyle by Amy Ramos

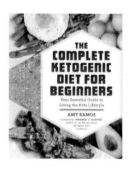

Other Great Books:

Living Low Carb: Controlled-Carbohydrate Eating for Long-Term Weight Loss by Jonny Bowden and Barry Sears

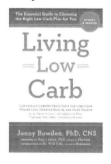

Cookbooks

2023 Annual Low-Carb Awards

1st Place Winner: The DIRTY, LAZY, KETO 5-Ingredient Cookbook: 100 Easy-Peasy Recipes Low in Carbs, Big on Flavor by Stephanie Laska (Author), William Laska (Author)

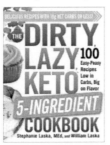

2nd Place Winner: Southern Keto: 100+ Traditional Food Favorites for a Low-Carb Lifestyle Paperback by Natasha Newton

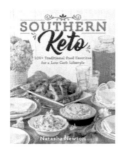

3rd Place Winner:

Low Carb Yum 5-Ingredient Keto: 120+ Easy Recipes

by Lisa MarcAurele

Runner Up:

Ketotarian: The (Mostly) Plant-Based Plan to Burn Fat, Boost Your Energy, Crush Your Cravings, and Calm Inflammation: A Cookbook by Dr. Will Cole (Author)

Other Great Cookbooks:

The Ultimate Guide to Keto Baking: Master All the Best Tricks for Low-Carb Baking Success by Carolyn Ketchum

The Easy 5-Ingredient Ketogenic Diet Cookbook: Low-Carb, High-Fat Recipes for Busy People on the Keto Diet by Jen Fisch

Media

Blogs & Websites

2023 Annual Low-Carb Awards

1st Place Winner: Low Carb Yum

LOW-CARB KETO RECIPES & RESOURCES

KETO DINNERS   KETO DESSERTS   KETO SIDES   KETO   LOW CARB   KETO

2nd Place Winner: All Day I Dream About Food

KETO AND LOW-CARB RECIPES!

Dreaming of truly delicious keto friendly recipes? You've come to the right place. I'm conjuring up low carb and sugar-free dishes that rival your old favorites. Everything from easy flavorful dinners to gorgeous keto desserts. Make keto fun again!

RECENT RECIPES

Hot off the presses! Check out all the latest and greatest keto recipes here.

3rd Place Winner: Peace Love and Low Carb

LOW-CARB, KETO, PALEO, & WHOLE30 RECIPES!

BROWSE BY DIET

Runner Up:

No Bun Please

Other Great Blogs & Websites:

Keto In The City

Traveling Low Carb

Low Carb with Jennifer

Mobile Apps

2023 Annual Low-Carb Awards

1st Place Winner: My Fitness Pal

2nd Place Winner: Carb Manager

3rd Place Winner: Lifesum

Runner Up:

Stupid Simple Keto

Other Great Apps:

Cronometer

Podcasts

2023 Annual Low-Carb Awards

1st Place Winner: Keto for Normies

2nd Place Winner: The Keto Diet Podcast with Leanne Vo-
gel

3rd Place Winner: The Livin' La Vida Low-Carb Show with
Jimmy Moore

Runner Up:

Low Carb MD Podcast

Other Great Podcasts:

Dirty, Lazy, Keto

Other

Butter / Ghee

2023 Annual Low-Carb Awards

1st Place Winner: ALDI-exclusive Carlini Ghee Clarified Butter

2nd Place Winner: BulletProof Grass-Fed Ghee

3rd Place Winner: Organic Valley Ghee

Comfort Foods

2023 Annual Low-Carb Awards

1st Place Winner: Fiber Gourmet Mac and Cheese

2nd Place Winner: Hu Chocolate Bars Salty Dark Chocolate

3rd Place Winner: Enlightened Peanut Butter Cookie Brownie Dough Ice Cream

Runner Up:

BariWise High Protein Hot Cocoa

Other Great Products:

Rebel Mint Chip

New Products

2023 Annual Low-Carb Awards

1st Place Winner: Shrewd Food Dark Chocolate Keto Dippers

2nd Place Winner: Flock Chicken Chips

3rd Place Winner: immi Low Carb Ramen

Runner Up:

Munk Pack Granola Bars

Other Great Products:

Project 7 Candy

Pasta, Sides, Soup & Sauces

Macaroni and Cheese

2023 Annual Low-Carb Awards

1st Place Winner: BANZA Chickpea Mac and Cheese

2nd Place Winner: Fiber Gourmet Mac and Cheese - Healthy & Cheesy Macaroni Noodles

3rd Place Winner: WonderSlim High Protein Diet Macaroni & Cheese Pasta

Pastas Brands

2023 Annual Low-Carb Awards

1st Place Winner: Already Spaghetti

2nd Place Winner: Banza

3rd Place Winner: Palmini

Runner Up:

Holista

Other Great Products:

Fiber Gourmet Pasta

fiber
gourmet

Condiments

2023 Annual Low-Carb Awards

1st Place Winner: Heinz No Sugar Added Tomato Ketchup

2nd Place Winner: G Hughes Sugar Free Ketchup

3rd Place Winner: Chosen Foods Classic Avocado Oil Mayo

Runner Up:

Sir Kensington's Avocado Oil Mayo

Other Great Products:

Primal Kitchen Spicy Ketchup

Dips and Spreads

2023 Annual Low-Carb Awards

1st Place Winner: Skinnygirl Sugar Free Apricot Mimosa Preserves

2nd Place Winner: Chia Smash - Raspberry Jam

3rd Place Winner: Diabetic Kitchen Sugar Free Hazelnut Cocoa Spread

Runner Up:

Left Coast Keto Peanut Butter with Macadamia Nuts and MCT Oil

Other Great Products:

ChocZero Keto White Chocolate Hazelnut Spread

Dressing

2023 Annual Low-Carb Awards

1st Place Winner: Skinnygirl Balsamic Vinaigrette Salad Dressing

2nd Place Winner: Primal Kitchen Avocado Oil Honey Mustard Dressing

3rd Place Winner: G Hughes Sugar Free Italian Dressing

Runner Up:

Yo Mama's Foods Ranch Salad Dressing

Other Great Products:

G Hughes Sugar Free Asian Miso Dressing

Sauces

2023 Annual Low-Carb Awards

1st Place Winner: G Hughes Sugar Free Polynesian Sauce

2nd Place Winner: Primal Kitchen Unsweetened Classic BBQ Sauce

3rd Place Winner: G Hughes Sugar Free Sweet Chili Sauce

Runner Up:

Noble Made by The New Primal Smoky BBQ Sauce

Other Great Products:

G Hughes Sugar Free Sweet Honey Wing Sauce

Sweet Baby Ray's No Sugar BBQ sauce

Soup

2023 Annual Low-Carb Awards

1st Place Winner: Kettle and Fire Broccoli Cheddar Keto Soup

2nd Place Winner: BariWise High Protein Low-Carb Chicken with Pasta Diet Soup Mix

3rd Place Winner: WonderSlim Protein Soup Mix - Chicken & Vegetable Cream Soup

Runner Up:

ProtiDIET Chicken Noodle Soup

Other Great Products:

WonderSlim Protein Soup Mix Tomato

Personalities

Best Low-Carb Personality

2023 Annual Low-Carb Awards

1st Place Winner: Carolyn Ketchum from All Day I Dream About Food

2nd Place Winner: Lisa MarcAurele from Low Carb Yum

3rd Place Winner: Mayra Wendolyne from @low.carb.love

Runner Up:

Jackie Harlaub from @lowcarbstateofmind

Other great Low-Carb people:

Chrissy Petty from @keto_buns

Janell Rohner from janellerohner.com

Pernilla Stryker from @pernillastryker

Low-Carb Product Registration

By submitting your products into The Low-Carb Awards (LCA), you are automatically entering products into the Annual Low-Carb Buyers Guide. There are only 10 slots available in each category and we limit brands to 3 submissions per category. If you are a marketer representing multiple brands, this typically will not apply. Slots can fill quickly so we recommend submitting your registration ASAP. The absolute deadline for registration is June 30th however, we cannot guarantee you that the category is already full.

"How do I get into the Low-Carb Awards?"

How it works:

1. Fill out the registration form by adding the quantities and product names.

(A free half page ad is given for every 5 products or full-page ad for 10 products.)

2. If wanted, add additional ad space to registration.

3. Email the registration form to Jayme@TheGuidedBuyer.com

4. We will follow up with a confirmation and invoice.

If you have any questions call customer support at 828-455-9734

"Wait, I have tons of questions still"

Most common questions:

Q: I am having a hard time understanding how to submit or products.

A: Using this Registration Form will help. If lost, don't hesitate to call or email. 828-455-9734

Q: What are the image specs you need?

A: Our graphic team just needs images that are PDF, JPEG or PNG at 300 dpi or greater. The team will normally resize images based on the publishing media. Normally the product pictures and descriptions from your website will work just fine.

Full Page Ad Size 384 by 576 px

Half Page Ad Size 384 by 288 px

Q: Is there a word count for product descriptions?

A: No, we normally don't use product descriptions just product names and images.

Q: If we submit 10 products do, we get 1 free full-page ad and 2 free half page ads?

A: Sorry, please choose one or the other. You can always purchase additional ad space.

Q: Can we run a full-page ad without entering the awards program?

A: Yes.

Q: Do we need to send you product samples?

A: No. The community votes for your products.

Q: Will we be in the guide if we don't win an award?

A: Yes, all products submitted will be visible as nominees.

Q: Can we use the LCA Nominee and Winner Badge on our product packaging, website and other related media?

A: Yes, we highly recommend using the badges to differentiate your products from the rest. If you happen to need higher resolution images don't hesitate to ask. Read our media terms here.

Need to talk about your order or have questions? Give us a call.

828-455-9734

or email

Josh@TheGuidedBuyer.com

From our family to yours, have a happy and healthy Low-Carb lifestyle.

The Schieffer Family

Josh (Dad with Celiac) Chief Marketing Officer

Jayme (Mom) VP Operations

Blake (22)

Jacob (18 Celiac)

Keep up to date with us, the awards, and future buyer guides at TheGuidedBuyer.com

Notes:

Notes:

Notes:

Notes: